The Bride's Book

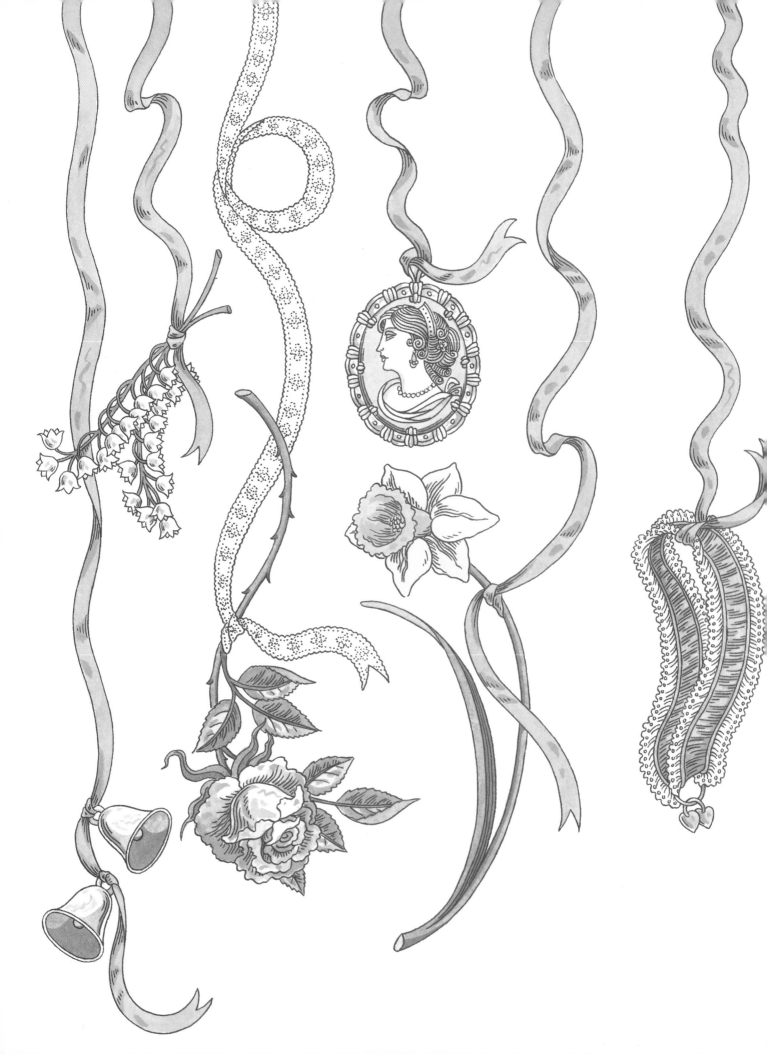

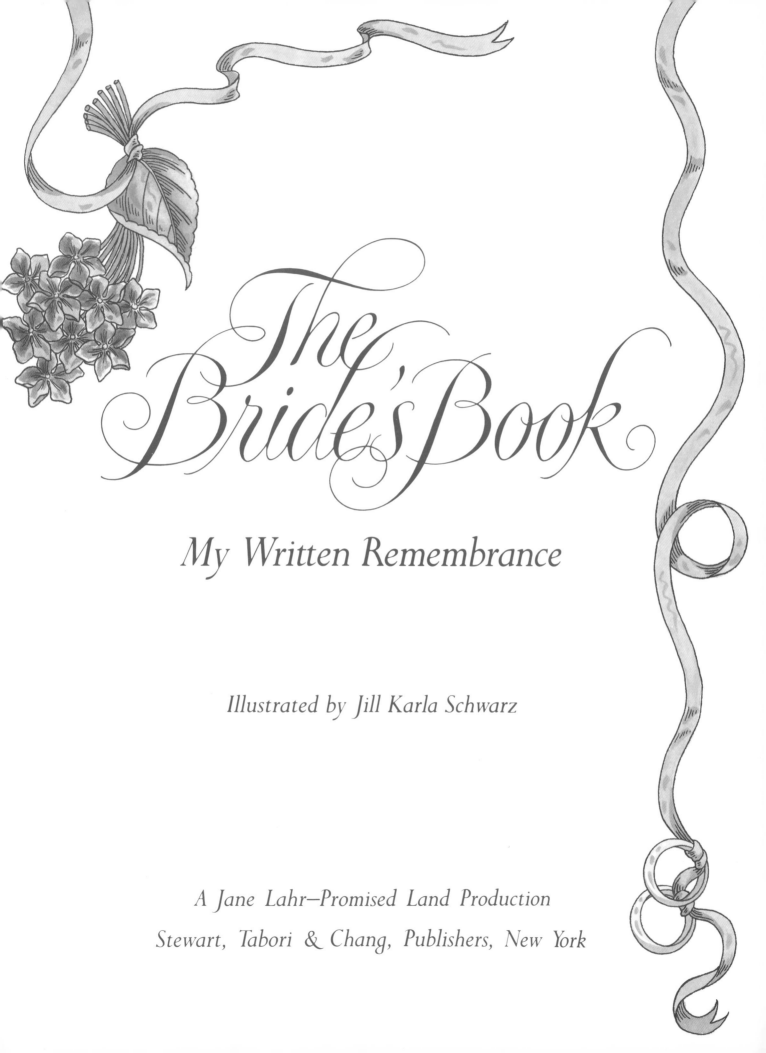

The Bride's Book

My Written Remembrance

Illustrated by Jill Karla Schwarz

A Jane Lahr–Promised Land Production

Stewart, Tabori & Chang, Publishers, New York

My maiden name _____

My married name _____

Date _____

Date of our wedding _____

Contents

THE LANGUAGE OF FLOWERS · 8

ALL ABOUT US · 10

FIRST IMPRESSIONS · 12

THE WORLD WE SHARE · 14

OUR FAMILIES · 16

THE PROPOSAL · 20

ENGAGEMENT CELEBRATIONS · 22

ENGAGEMENT MEMORIES · 24

WEDDING TRADITIONS · 26

PLANNING OUR WEDDING · 28

MY WEDDING INVITATION · 30

THE GUEST LIST · 32

MY BRIDAL SHOWER · 36

MY BRIDAL REGISTRY · 37

GIVEN IN OUR HONOR · 38

OLD AND NEW, BORROWED AND BLUE · 40

OUR CEREMONY · 42

THE RECEPTION · 44

WEDDING MEMENTOS · 50

WEDDING GIFTS · 52

PHOTOGRAPHS · 54

OUR HONEYMOON · 58

OUR LIFE TOGETHER · 60

OUR FUTURE TOGETHER · 62

OUR FIRST ANNIVERSARY · 64

The Language of Flowers

A NOTE TO THE BRIDE

From the beginning of civilization, flowers have been seen as symbols of beauty, feelings, and ceremony. By the nineteenth century, the symbolism of each flower was so well known that flowers had become the language of love. Books called The Language of Flowers *were presented as tokens of their intentions by men and women alike, in an age when it was considered impolite or forward to express love directly. Today, while we no longer need to hide our feelings, the connection between the beauty of flowers and the wonder of love remains.*

The ancient meanings of flowers are romantic, and they still apply. So, on many pages of this book flowers appear, each with its own special meaning. On the opposite page we offer a list of the flowers, along with their traditional meanings, that have been used throughout your book.

Congratulations, and may your life be filled with flowers.

THE EDITORS

A Single Rose	*Simplicity*
Lily of the Valley	*Return of Happiness*
Rose	*Love*
Daffodil	*Regard*
Blue Violet	*Faithfulness*
Plum Blossom	*Fidelity*
Tulip	*Declaration of Love*
Iris	*Message*
Orchid	*A Belle*
Garden Daisy	*I Share Your Sentiments*
Lily	*Sweetness*
Lilac	*First Emotions of Love*
Ivy	*Ties*
Water Lily	*Purity of Heart*
Clover	*Think of Me*
Pear	*Affections*
Apple Blossom	*Preference*
White Calla Lily	*Magnificent Beauty*
White Violet	*Candor*
Bachelor Button	*Hope in Love*
Blue Larkspur	*Levity*
Crocus	*Mirth*
Moss Rosebud	*Confession of Love*
Hibiscus	*Delicate Beauty*
Phlox	*Unanimity*

All About Us

My full name is _____

_____

I was born on _____ at _____

_____

_____

I went to school at _____

_____

_____

I am now working as _____

_____

_____

My hobbies are _____

_____

_____

I most enjoy _____

_____

_____

My fiancé's full name is _____

_____

He was born on _____ at _____

_____

_____

He went to school at _____

_____

_____

He now works as _____

_____

_____

His hobbies are _____

_____

_____

He most enjoys _____

_____

_____

11

First Impressions

No sooner met but they looked, no
Sooner looked, but they loved.

SHAKESPEARE

I first met my husband-to-be on _____ at _____

_____

I was wearing _____

_____

_____

I dazzled him with _____

_____

_____

I was attracted to him because _____

_____

_____

_____

_____

We talked about _____

_____

_____

_____

_____

I fell for him when _____

_____

We first kissed _____

_____

I knew I wanted to marry him when _____

_____

_____

The World We Share

Let me not to the marriage of true minds
Admit impediments.

SHAKESPEARE

*We care most about*_____

_____

_____

*The friends we have in common are*_____

_____

_____

*The most romantic evening we've spent was*_____

_____

_____

*The best holiday we've shared was*_____

_____

_____

*The best meal we've ever had was*_____

_____

_____

*The sports we enjoy together are*_____

_____

_____

*Our favorite songs are*_____

_____

*The hobbies we share are*_____

_____

_____

*The best movies we've seen together are*_____

_____

_____

*The things that bring us closer are*_____

_____

_____

*The traits we have in common are*_____

_____

_____

Our Families

My mother _____

_____

My father _____

_____

My sisters _____

_____

My brothers _____

_____

My maternal grandmother _____

_____

My maternal grandfather _____

_____

My paternal grandmother _____

_____

My paternal grandfather _____

_____

My aunts _____

_____

My uncles _____

_____

His father_____

_____

His mother_____

_____

His brothers_____

_____

His sisters_____

_____

His paternal grandfather_____

_____

His paternal grandmother_____

_____

His maternal grandfather_____

_____

His maternal grandmother_____

_____

His uncles_____

_____

His aunts_____

_____

My father's family originally came from_____

_____

_____

_____

My mother's family originally came from_____

_____

_____

_____

My parents met on_____at_____

_____

_____

_____

My parents were married on_____at_____

_____

_____

_____

My mother was_____ years old and my father was_____

_____

18

His father's family originally came from _____

_____

_____

_____

His mother's family originally came from _____

_____

_____

_____

His parents met on _____ at _____

_____

_____

_____

His parents were married on _____ at _____

_____

_____

_____

His mother was _____ years old and his father was _____

_____

19

The Proposal

Come live with me and be my love.
CHRISTOPHER MARLOWE

*My fiancé proposed to me on*_____

  *while we were*_____

_____

*I will always remember*_____

_____

_____

*The words I'll never forget were*_____

_____

_____

I rushed to tell _____

_____

_____

My best friend's exact words were _____

_____

_____

_____

20

When we told my parents, my mother said_____

_____

and my father said_____

_____

When we told my fiancé's parents, they said_____

_____

_____

My parents and my fiancé's parents met on_____

at_____

To mark our engagement, my fiancé gave me_____

_____

and I gave him_____

_____

We announced our engagement on_____

_____

_____

21

Engagement

Drink to me only with thine eyes,
And I will pledge with mine;

We celebrated by _____

_____

_____

_____

_____

Our families celebrated by _____

_____

_____

_____

_____

Other celebrations were given in our honor by _____

_____

_____

_____

_____

_____

_____

_____

Celebrations

Or leave a kiss but in the cup
And I'll not look for wine.

BEN JONSON

Gifts we received for our engagement were _____

_____

_____

_____

_____

_____

_____

_____

_____

The engagement ring we selected was _____

_____

_____

_____

_____

_____

_____

_____

_____

23

Engagement Memories

ANNOUNCEMENTS

MEMENTOS

Wedding Traditions

...And let them also with them bring
in hand,
Another gay garland
For my fair love of lilies and roses,
Bound true-love-wise with a blue
silk ribbon...

EDMUND   SPENSER

My family traditionally celebrates weddings by _____

_____

_____

_____

_____

My fiancé's family traditionally celebrates weddings by_____

_____

_____

_____

_____

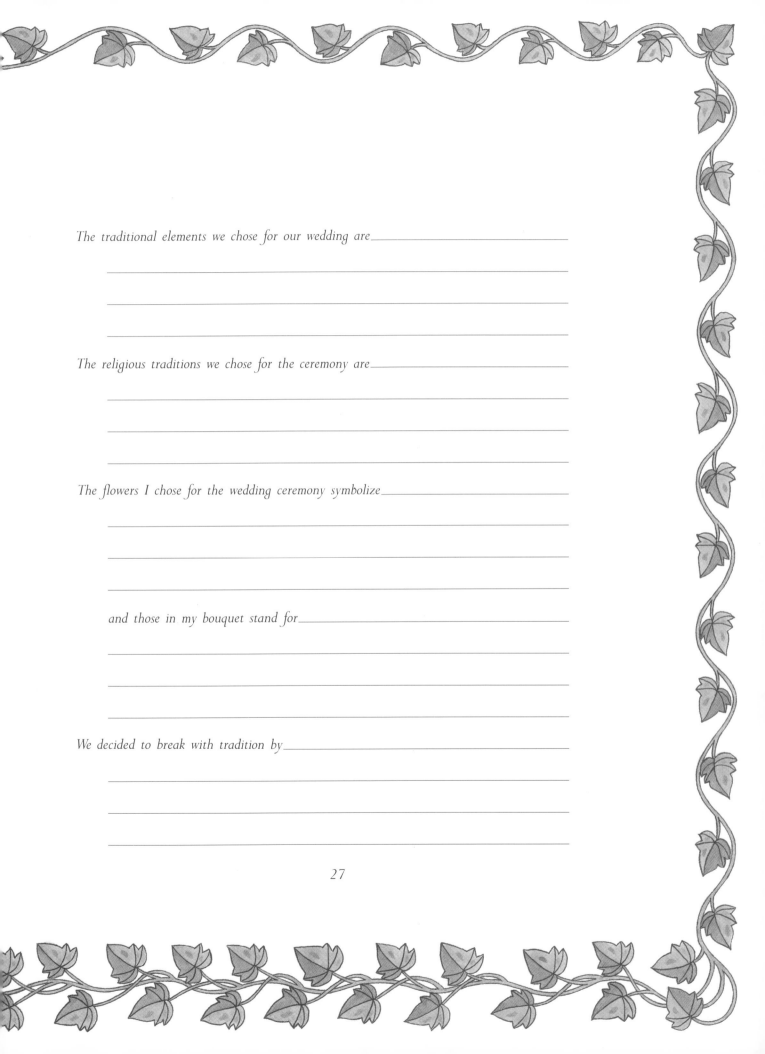

*The traditional elements we chose for our wedding are*_____

_____

_____

_____

*The religious traditions we chose for the ceremony are*_____

_____

_____

_____

*The flowers I chose for the wedding ceremony symbolize*_____

_____

_____

_____

*and those in my bouquet stand for*_____

_____

_____

_____

*We decided to break with tradition by*_____

_____

_____

_____

27

Planning Our Wedding

We decided to get married on _____

    at _____

_____

We asked _____ to perform the ceremony

    because _____

_____

I asked _____ to be my maid

    or matron of honor, and I chose as my attendants _____

_____

_____

My fiancé asked _____ to be his

    best man, and he chose as his ushers _____

_____

_____

We planned to have our reception at _____

_____

_____

28

The reception will be a_____

_____

The color theme will be_____

_____

The floral arrangements will be_____

_____

We selected_____music, played by_____

_____

_____

The menu will include_____

_____

_____

And will be prepared by_____

_____

_____

The cake will be created by_____

_____

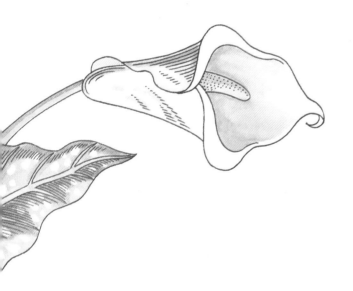

My Wedding

Invitation

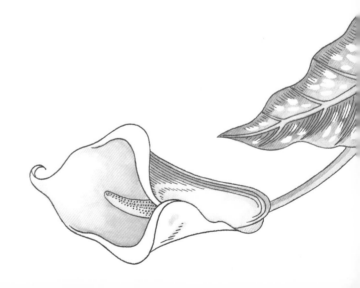

The Guest List

_____

_____

_____

_____

_____

_____

_____

_____

_____

_____

_____

_____

_____

_____

_____

_____

_____

_____

_____

_____

_____

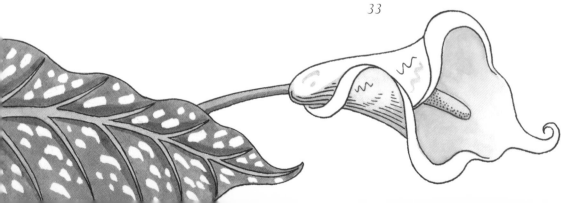

The Guest List

_____

_____

_____

_____

_____

_____

_____

_____

_____

_____

_____

_____

_____

_____

_____

_____

_____

_____

_____

_____

_____

My Bridal Shower

I prize thy love more than whole mines of gold,
Or all the riches that the East doth hold

ANNE   BRADSTREET

My bridal shower was given by _____

     on _____

     at _____

Guests were _____

_____

_____

_____

The theme of the shower was _____

_____

The funniest gift was _____

_____

The most useful gift was _____

_____

The most touching gift was _____

_____

The best moments were _____

_____

_____

36

My
Bridal Registry

China pattern _____

    Store _____

_____

_____

Flatware pattern _____

    Store _____

_____

_____

Crystal pattern _____

    Store _____

_____

_____

Glassware pattern _____

    Store _____

_____

Linen pattern _____

    Store _____

_____

_____

Given in Our Honor

Play, music. And you, brides
and bridegrooms all,
With measure heap'd in joy, to
the measures fall.

SHAKESPEARE

Luncheons_____

_____

_____

Dinners_____

_____

_____

_____

Parties_____

_____

_____

Bachelor party

Rehearsal dinner

Old and New,

My love hath my heart, and
I have his,

My wedding dress was_____

_____

_____

and my accessories were_____

_____

_____

I wore my hair_____

_____

My "old and new, borrowed and blue" were_____

_____

_____

_____

_____

Borrowed and Blue

By just exchange one for the
        other given.

SIR   PHILIP   SIDNEY

My attendants' dresses were _____

_____

_____

_____

and they carried _____

My husband wore _____

_____

with _____ as a boutonniere

His ushers wore _____

_____

The rings we exchanged were _____

_____

_____

Our Ceremony

Look, how my ring encompasseth thy finger,
Even so thy breast enclose my poor heart,
Wear both of them, for both of them are thine.

SHAKESPEARE

The readings for the ceremony were _____

_____

_____

_____

_____

When we exchanged rings, we vowed _____

_____

_____

_____

_____

_____

_____

The music was _____

_____

_____

_____

The most touching moment was _____

_____

_____

_____

Unplanned moments that made the ceremony very special were _____

_____

_____

_____

I knew we were married when _____

_____

_____

The Reception

MENU

Appetizers

_____

_____

First Course

_____

_____

_____

Main Course

_____

_____

_____

Dessert

_____

_____

_____

Wines

_____
_____
_____

Wedding Cake

_____
_____
_____
_____
_____
_____
_____
_____

45

The Reception

MOMENTS TO REMEMBER

The first toast was given by _____

_____

who said _____

_____

_____

_____

_____

_____

The best toast was given by _____

_____

who said _____

_____

_____

_____

_____

_____

_____

_____

_____

*The moments and comments worth preserving for posterity were*_____

_____

_____

_____

_____

_____

_____

_____

_____

_____

_____

*When we cut the cake*_____

_____

_____

*I danced the first dance with*_____

_____

_____

*My husband and I danced to*_____

_____

_____

_____

The Reception

MOMENTS TO REMEMBER

Some of the special friends who came were_____

_____

_____

_____

_____

_____

_____

_____

_____

_____

_____

_____

My bouquet was caught by_____

_____

_____

My garter was caught by_____

_____

_____

I especially remember _____

_____

_____

_____

_____

_____

_____

_____

_____

_____

We decided to leave at _____

_____

_____

I wore _____

_____

_____

We left in _____

_____

_____

_____

49

Wedding

Mementos

Wedding Gifts

Our gifts to our attendants were _____

_____

_____

_____

_____

_____

_____

Our gifts to each other were _____

_____

_____

_____

_____

_____

_____

Gifts we received

From

53

Photographs

Photographs

Photographs

Photographs

Our Honeymoon

Happy, thrice happy and more,
are they whom an unbroken bond unites.

HORACE

We spent our wedding night at_____

_____

We honeymooned from_____to_____

_____

We went to_____

_____

DAY-TO-DAY DIARY

Day one_____

_____

_____

Day two_____

_____

_____

Day three_____

_____

_____

Day four _____

_____

_____

Day five _____

_____

_____

Day six _____

_____

_____

Day seven _____

_____

Our Life Together

Gentle love deeds, as blossoms on a bough,
From love's awaken'd root do bud out now.

JOHN   DONNE

Our new address is _____

_____

_____

We "warmed" our home by _____

_____

_____

Our color scheme is _____

_____

_____

Our first major purchase was _____

_____

_____

60

We celebrated our first holiday by _____
_____
_____
_____
_____

Our first guests were _____
_____
_____
_____
_____

Other firsts were _____
_____
_____
_____
_____
_____
_____
_____
_____

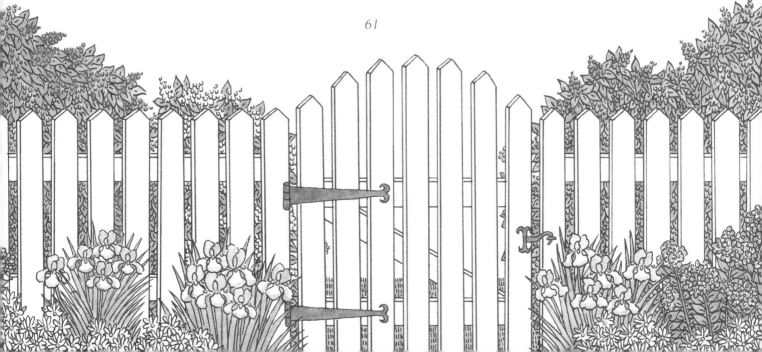

Our Future Together

*Our plans and dreams for the future include*_____

_____

_____

_____

_____

_____

_____

_____

_____

_____

_____

_____

_____

Our First Anniversary

If ever two were one, then surely we.
If ever man were lov'd by wife, then thee;
If ever wife was happy in a man...

ANNE BRADSTREET

We celebrated our first anniversary by _____

_____

_____

The gifts we gave each other were _____

_____

_____

The best times of our first year were _____

_____

_____

The experiences that brought us closer were _____

_____

_____

We hope our second year will bring us _____

_____

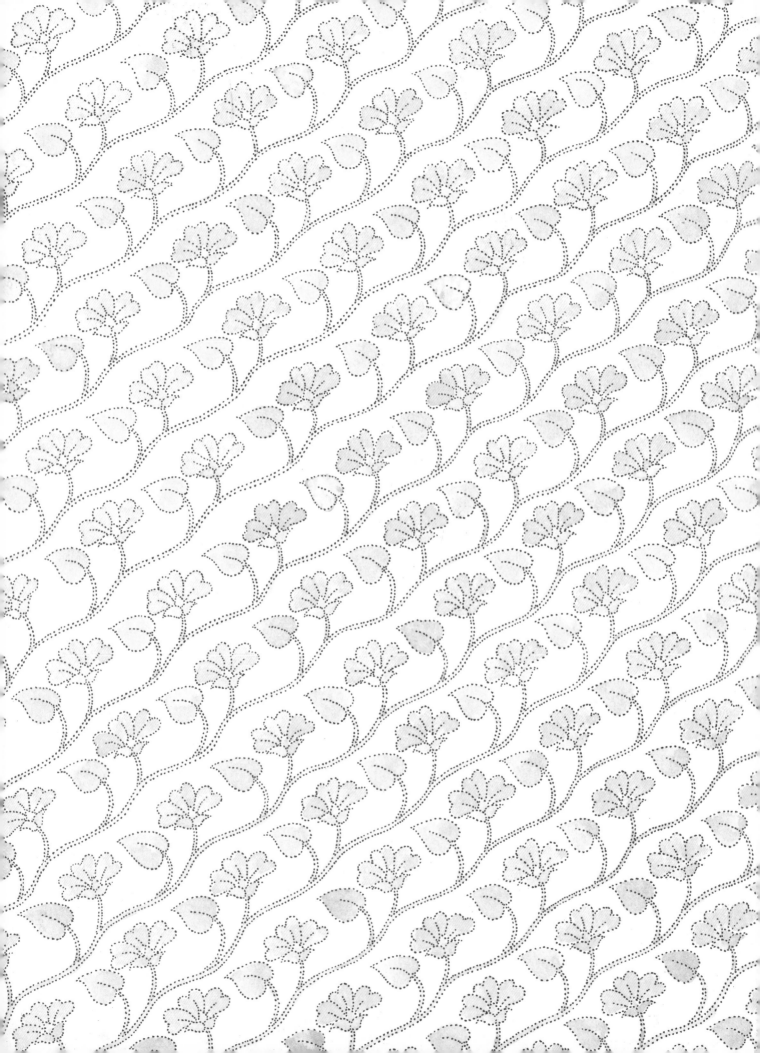